landing
like
rain

by

audrey wilson

ISBN (paperback): 979-8-9903632-3-6
ISBN (hard cover): 979-8-9903632-5-0

Library of Congress Control Number: 1-13655493121

Any references to historical events, real people, or real places
are used fictitiously. Names, characters, and places are products
of the author's imagination.

Illustrations and front cover design by Audrey Wilson.
Additional illustration for "Because" by Sharon Wilson.
Headshot by Jennifer Mayo.

Generative AI was not used in any form in the drafting, editing,
design, or production of this book.

Printed in the United States of America.

First printing edition 2024.

www.AudreyWilsonAuthor.com

Praise for *landing like rain*

"Embark on a journey through the myriad forms of love
with *landing like rain*, these poignant tales illuminate the
power of words to heal the heart. This gem is a tender
reminder that love, in all its forms, has the strength to
mend even the deepest wounds."
~ ANN GARVIN, *USA Today* bestselling author
of *There's No Coming Back From This*

"Wilson's poetry is varied and heartfelt. With sadness,
happiness, longing, and every emotion in tow, this book is a
spectrum of feelings all wrapped up in a neat package."
~ TINA P. SCHWARTZ, author & literary agent

Table of Contents

For those who love.

Falling.

Love

Whether in falling or fancy,
It is Love that gives us joy,
That aches our hearts,
Entices our spirits;
In forces as strong as the current,
And wisps of smoke
Never to be pinned.

It is the impatience
That shows no end,
The ticking clock that passes
At an unrequited pace,
And it is a moment, fleeting
From our tired hands,
Falling in drops
Like rain upon soft skin,
And drying up
With the faintest trace
Of sun.

It is counted in our blessings,
Held contented in the stars,
It shoots through the sky
From Cupid's burning bow,
Caring not who the broken heart
Has loved before,
Nor who it chooses to unite
In its second wind.
Instead, Love stays ever-present;
The rain, the sun, the wind, the stars,
Even the moon cannot restrain.
In the air we breathe, the hearts we hold,
Love, forevermore, remains.

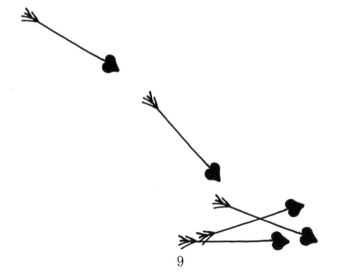

One Too Much

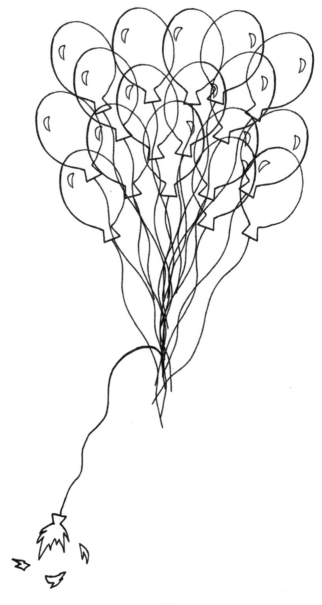

Barry, you're lovely.
Simon, don't stop.
Marry me, Jason?
Time's beating the clock.
Harry, you're boring.
Steven, you're late.
Austin, don't tease me.
Forget it, it's great.
Billy, I love you.
Randy, I need you.
Walter, make all of my
wedding dreams come true.
Harold, you're kind.
Joe, you're quite nice.
But, Larry, you've got both
that sugar and spice.
Carl, great cooking.
Sam, nice cleaning.
Justin, you give my whole life
such meaning.
Jim, gorgeous roses.
Kip, stunning ring.
Adam, you're perfect
if you just wouldn't sing.
Now, won't you please stay.
Nevermind, just go.
I'm tired of waiting
for one of you to say, "No."
You've all been so perfect
You've all had that touch
And though one's never enough
Eighteen's one too much.

I want to write a poem
For you that says it all
But throwing out the words
Would risk making them fall.
I want to whisper softly
For you alone to hear
But my spoken words are drowned
In vainly driven fear.
I want to paint a picture
Using colors bold and bright
But painting with such loudness
Might blind you from the sight.
I want to sing and shout
Words I'd never say aloud
Still the only time I'll say them
Is when you're not around.
I wish that I could show you
All this artwork that I keep
Trying to tell you that I love you
In hopes that you'll love me.

Only One

Knee-high boots
Long red hair
Hiding her secret smile.
When she speaks,
She takes my breath
Makes me feel things
I didn't know I could.
Behind her
The dusty chalkboard
Frames her silhouette
Gentle curves
move beneath
Her clingy woven dress
The fabric
I can imagine so well
Beneath my fingertips
But as I face her
She faces us
Our sight is not aligned
I see her as one
Only one
But to her
I'm one of twenty-five.

The Right Way

A million miles away
Lives the girl next door
Hiding her heart
Till she can't anymore.
Luxuriously silky
Are her pillows and sheets
Yet she turns and she tosses
Whenever she sleeps.
Biting on faith
She's still young and fecund
But finds her life over
Before it's begun.

She searches for doorways
To find a way out
Can't see she's the sun
Behind the gray clouds.
They say she shouldn't give up
That love marches on
But love has two sides
And one side is wrong.
Vehemently scorching
Are the cold eyes that see
Two girls holding hands
And decide what can't be.

Two of the Same

Two wishful dreamers
Together flew
Into the starry starry night,
But lost themselves
In the dreams they drew
With their heads adrift in the skies.

Two stubborn realists
Hands pocketed, stood
Seeing a dark, deserted land,
Not once seeing the beauty,
The hope or the good,
They could have built with their pocketed hands.

Two light silly hearts
Off together ran
Their happiness piercing the sky,
Laughing and giggling
Till one day near the end
They realized they forgot how to cry.

Two lonely loners
Alone in the dark
Sat never speaking a word,
Never once calling out
For a hand or a heart
Never knowing an ear would have heard.

Yet two hopeless romantics
Together fell
Into a love like no one knew,
And though two of the same,
Their hopeless hearts did meld
Never once falling in two.

Landing Like Rain

There are no words between us,
only a shared thought binding our minds.
The roads, empty but slick.
The windows, frosted with thinly veiled fog.
My heart, pounding beneath my dress.
Yours, beside me, patiently waiting,
Impatiently, beating.
In a moment, we've stopped
In a moment, we're frozen,
our minds still bound by a single thought.
On the radio, a different song plays for each of us.
If we wait a moment longer,
the moment will have passed.
But you don't let it.
My face in your hands,
Your lips on mine.
I'll never leave.
I simply can't.
Even as I stand,
willing my legs to carry me,
my heart stays with yours.
With your lips in my head,
my lightness carries me home,
pieces of the April sky around me,
falling like snow
and landing like rain.

Apart.

Midnight

The bare trees scratch
At midnight's darkest hour,
The hairs of the branches
Hitting the grass
In the moon's broken lamp.
Without sound or fury,
The air hangs still,
Waiting for sunrise
To wash out the flames placed
So perfectly
In the blackness.
I wait amongst the limbs
To see the face burned in me,
That brings out all I know
To be good and honest and true,
The only falsities in blind reality.
And although filled time has passed me by
I have not yet found that piece of you
That touches something in me,
But I do know, with all truth,
That the place I hold in your heart,
Is not the same in mine.
Naked limbs crossing path for path
And fire against the night sky.

The House of Broken Hearts

Grass burnt orange
In a field of memories
Left for God's vanity beside
The House of Broken Hearts.
Skies of perfect white
Are muddied by gray,
Clouded by life
And hung out to dry.
Left behind
Is a gown of soft peach,
Shredding,
Against scratched brown.

She presses on,
Still,
Knowing all that waits
Are the tattered panels,
The damaged steps,
The tracks she never should have followed,
And everything else
That builds
The House of Broken Hearts.
But still,
She presses on.

Dead Weight

Etta's stride was brisk even in the hot Alabama sun. She made her way across the field of wheat to the source of the ruckus and found Halsey in a clearing. He was kneeling beside a large white mass.

"What in God's name have you done?" Her voice was shrill as the crows above them.

The young farmhand got to his feet and removed his cap in the presence of his employer.

"Ain't done nothing, ma'am. Horse was dead when I got here." He avoided her eyes and wrung the cap in his hands.

"For God's sake, Halsey–" The words gagged in her throat when she caught the first scent of the animal's corpse. "Just how do you think Gertie's going to take this?"

"I'm terribly sorry, ma'am." The hat was beginning to shred at the corners. "Just found him this way, I swear I did."

"Quit cowering and get the tractor."

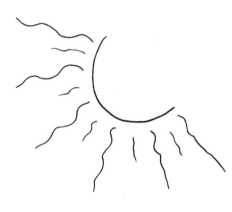

The boy took off through the fields at a run. By this time Etta had her handkerchief out. She shook it with a faint crack and used it to mask her face from the odor, then knelt down beside the animal's head to feel for a pulse. His black eyes were round and open, like the shock that his life was over had just hit him. She cursed under her breath.

Halsey came out from the wheat with no tractor.

Etta got to her feet. "Where is it?"

"Not starting." He wiped the sweat from his brow and breathed hard and fast. "We'll drag him."

"You'll drag him." She brushed the dirt off her hands, smugness creeping over her already stern features. "Ladies don't do that sort of work."

"My apologies for suggesting anything different, ma'am." His cap was now shoved awkwardly into his pants pocket. For the first time in four weeks he made eye contact with the woman. "I ain't never aiming to harm you."

Before she could let her guard down, she built it back up. "Fine," she said. "You have any rope?"

"I do." He went to his tool chest on the opposite side of the clearing and pulled out a thick rope. The two tied it securely around the animal with proper knotting and balance. They kept the silence between them dead as the body at their feet. When they were done, Halsey went to the front and wrapped the rope around his arms. The low sun signaled the day was coming to an end.

He pulled forward and the horse's body dragged on the ground with his lead. Etta stood still for a moment. She couldn't remember the last time she just stood. Without allowing herself to think, she moved to the front of the horse next to Halsey and took hold of a free-hanging rope.

"You don't gotta do that, ma'am."

"Stop calling me ma'am."

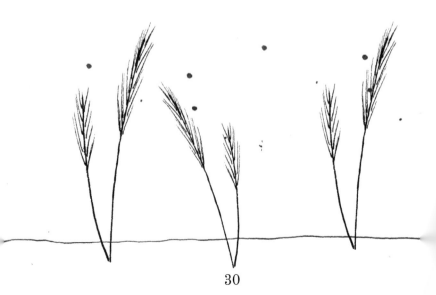

The silence rose again as the two drug the animal over the wheat and away from the barn.

"I still been having dreams about you," Halsey said, looking straight ahead.

"You'll have to stop that."

"I can't," he said. "You're in my head and I can't get you out."

Etta didn't say anything. The sun was hotter than ever and she could feel her whole body sweating under her long dress. Her arms ached from pulling, but she didn't complain. Halsey kept his eyes forward, like he was looking ahead for an answer he couldn't find. In the heat and haze, she felt his hand on hers. She didn't pull it away, but she didn't take it either.

"Dreams are dreams," she said finally, breaking the connection. "They may have been memories at one point in time, but now they're dead weight. Nothing more."

He didn't hold her hand again after that, but kept a firm grasp on the ropes and pulled with all he had.

Waves

Crashing waves
    And passing days
        Drag slowly across the sand,
            Salty air
                And sun-kissed hair
                    Lost on naked, empty hands.

Rocky beach
    Shells, one of each
        Strewn with no reason or rhyme,
           Only parts
               Of our broken hearts
                   Lost forever in this sea of mine.

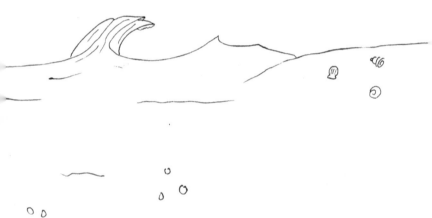

I hear you call
    You hear me fall
        Crawling on the ocean floor,
          My breath, I lose
            My patience, few
               For I can swim no more.

Haircut

I.)
I got my hairs cut today
By a lady in a blue dress.
She smelled like Mommy's powder
Daddy's cigarettes
And hairspray that stickies my face.
I watched the cut ones
Hit the apron around my neck
And made sure to bounce them off
Each time they landed
With my secret hands under the sheet.
I didn't tell the lady
The collar was buttoned up too tight
Cause Mommy always says
The stiller I sit
The quieter I am
The sooner I can go outside and play.

II.)
I had my hair done today
At the corner of State and Madison.
Thirteen women around me
Talking fast
Telling me how beautiful
I was going to look in white.
The man with the curling-iron
Talked faster than the girls
His hands dancing with each word he sang.
I wore my mother's aging pearls
Tight around my neck
The newest band of silver
Circled my finger with a promise
My sister's favorite anklet
Hung loosely near the ground
And in my hair a flower of teal
Attempted to mimic something blue.

III.)
I had them cut it first
Because secretly I'd always wondered
What I'd look like with a pixie
And now was as good a time as any.
All but an inch of the dark brown
Was chopped and styled.
I looked at myself in the glass
My eyes, for the first time, open
To the beauty I'd never seen.
But as with any form of beauty
The patches were still visible
And I had them shave it all
And take away the mirror.
With a primary blue bandanna
Wrapped around my head,
I took the hand beside me
And walked through glass to light.

IV.)
My hair was done today
By a man with tender hands
He rolled each strand
With perfect care
And placed a white flower
Behind a curl.
They laid me down
In a bed of silk
With a frame of deep cherry wood
Beside a vase of red roses
And mourners dressed in black.
I wore my favorite blue dress
And my mother's aging pearls,
The tarnished silver band,
Still gently holding my finger.
With time still passing
I hold on to all I had
Only wishing
I hadn't held it all so tightly.

The Normal Family

In a little blue house
By a little green tree
Lives the Normal Family
Of Everyday Street.

Mrs. Normal spends
The time of her day
Cooking and cleaning
While the kids are away.
She washes the dishes
Cleans dirty clothes
Follows directions
Does all that she's told.
When she starts to grow tired
And feels any pain
She finds comfort with John
And the Barleycorn gang.
She powders her nose
With patience and time
To cover the wear
And hide all the lines
Then paints on a smile
To bury the gray
And she does it all
While the kids are away.

Sue and Jim Normal
Follow the rules
They keep their rooms clean
Get good grades in school.
Jim cares for his sister
Like any big brother should
But hides in his closet
Where old toys once stood.
He runs from trouble
Where others say fight
He fears the dark
But won't sleep with a light.
He laughs with his buddies
About the queer boy in town
To keep appearances up
And push honesty down.

Little Sue Normal
Can hold up her own
She's too smart for her classmates
And likes being alone.
No words can break her
No stones can bruise
She'll play if she wins
And run if she'll lose.
She's perfectly happy
Her life is complete
Yet she can't understand
Why she cries herself to sleep.

Still Sue and Jim Normal
Have everyone to fool
So they keep their rooms clean
Get good grades in school.

Mr. Normal works
Seven days of the week
Helping his secretary
Improve office technique.
He spins many webs
Trying to keep it all straight
And hopes his wife doesn't know
Why he has to work late.
He leaves home before dawn
Gets back after dark
Kisses his children
Feels a stab in his heart
He wipes the red lipstick
Off the collar of his shirt
Each time hopes the water
Will wash away the hurt.
He vows to do better
As he drifts off to sleep
But tomorrow does the same
Improving office technique.

They all sit at dinner
Showing only outsides
Each one pretending
They have nothing to hide.
They laugh and they smile
As they come and they go
So no one will notice
And no one will know.

Because these are the lives
That nobody sees
In the Normal Family
Of Everyday Street.

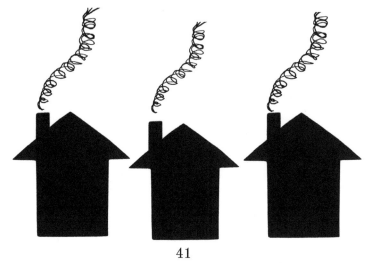

Pieces of Me

I will never piece together
the puzzle of my heart;
The fragments tossed around
by someone else's hand.
Now lost within pages,
hidden under beds,
damaged through years
of wear and play;
A game I never won.
Some days I'll find
a piece or two,
hiding under dust.
Each holding tight
a memory
of when you and I
were us.

But now I see those pieces
were never truly lost.
Just left alone, unfit,
staying the same
as when I left,
while I grow older
piece by piece.
Still I find I cannot sleep
until I put this puzzle to rest
knowing all they'll ever be;
Pieces of me,
Fragments of us.

Balance

You fly by the night
I climb through the trenches.
You spend with no money
I fret all expenses.
You tell me you love me
Then fall straight asleep.
I hear your soft words
And continue to dream.
You laugh till you cry
I laugh to hide tears.
You plan for today
I plan for the years.
You think only of me
Whenever we're one,
I think about you
Long after you're gone.

You catch all the stars
I'm hit with the showers
You worry for minutes
I do it for hours.
You hold onto me tight
No space in between.
I bury my face
To hide what's unseen.
You and I stand quite different
Sometimes on shaky ground
But in the end, we're still level;
We balance us out.

The Strength of Your Heart

Do not be afraid,
My Love,
to wake up every morning.
All you know
may feel lost
inside your mind,
but all you believe
is forever in your soul.
You are stronger than your past,
braver than your future.
And even through
your darkest nights
I know you'll wake
with hope and light
For even in
your hardest times
the strength of your heart
gives me strength
in mine.

Alone.

An Empty Mirror

A looking glass
you can't look into
without it looking
right back at you
A still water pond
you cannot see through
without it seeing
right back through you.

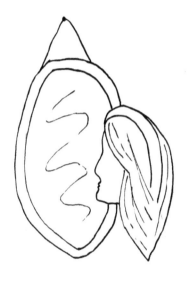

A clear glass window
as everyone knows
cannot be seen through
if it's closed.
An empty reflection
can never be clear
because there's no such thing
as an empty mirror.

Nights Like These

Bumps and bruises
from laughing too hard
in the earliest hours
of the morning.
Inside jokes,
looks that tell all,
unplanned,
unpredicted stories.
From tying up in knots
our limbs and our thoughts,
insanity disguised
with giggles.
To crowding on couches,
trying not to nod off
exhausted,
still fighting off tickles.

These are the moments
that make up my life,
that will make me smile
through the hardest times.
It's nights like these
that make me never forget
how lucky I am
these friends
are mine.

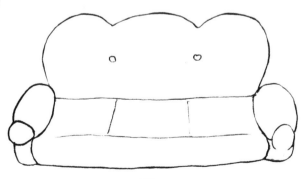

There Are No Words

There are no words. There is only the wind caressing my red cheeks. The stairs that lead out of the basement are glassed over, and I'm careful to only step on what I know is solid concrete. I don't like the feeling of lost control on the ice. It's too much like dancing, too much like falling. My hands are bare and holding the railing would only make them colder, so I have to keep my balance on my own.

There's a pair of black fleece mittens drying on the rail. I touch them, looking for something to warm my hands, but the mittens are still wet. They smell damp, of snow and leaves left over from fall. The smell takes me back, and I remember having to hang up all my wet winter clothes to dry after a long afternoon of playing outside. This was a time when it would take threats and bribes to get me to come in from playing games in the snow. That was back when games had no rules and my hands never got cold. Now life is nothing but rules and my hands always freeze.

My eyes graze the yard. Everything is dark. Only the porch lights on the distant houses across the iced creek and the snow-coated ground bring light to the darkness. My gaze stops on the snow. For a moment, the child within me that hides right below the surface shows itself, and I wonder what makes the snow so bright. In my mind's eye I see a hundred miniature lights shining up from the ground beneath the blanket, shining through from where grass had once been. Winter can be dull. With Spring and Summer desperate to come into view, taunting Winter with visions of sunshine and warmth, I guess he simply got tired of his days being so short, nights being so long, and decided to turn the ground into the sky after every sunset.

I stop the moment from carrying me away and guide my eyes upward until I catch the moon. They say you can tell direction from the moon. Or maybe it's the North Star. My consciousness is regained and I float back down to reality.

But reality is colder than I remember. I'm only wearing a sweater that's been washed too many times and jeans that haven't been washed enough. I wish I had a coat. There's a boy who shares his coat with me when the wind bites, and warms my hands when my fingers freeze. I try to make myself think that I can keep warm on my own. I can, and I have, but maybe I need to let someone else try this time. It's still cold outside, but inside I can feel myself warming up.

I take my first step off the cement and onto the snow. My foot breaks the surface and sinks down. There are no words. There is no traffic. All I hear is the crunching of the crushed ice under my soles. Each step, I think, is going to be different than the next. That I'm going to put down my weight and not sink four inches. Only fools think this way. I stop myself from thinking further.

I reach the edge of the yard and the beginning of the creek and see there's nowhere to go from here. I think maybe I'll draw a map and see where it takes me. A map doesn't need any words, only lines to destinations. You can't get lost if you have a map. The world can keep their words, I'll keep my map, and we'll call it even.

It's funny. I know just where I am, with no idea how I got here or where I'm going, and it's funny. I'm not cold. I'm not warm. I'm simply here, existing, trying with every ounce of strength I have not to get lost. Trying so hard can break a girl. Slowly, I begin to relax. There's something about my surroundings and the glowing earth that makes me feel safe and warm and comforted. Maybe it would be nice to let myself get lost every now and then. I don't need words to get lost. I don't need a coat to keep me warm, but it helps. Suddenly, I find myself forgetting the cold, losing my fears, and remembering everything I have. I don't know if it's the moon. I don't know if it's the snow. I don't know if they are two pieces or one, and I wonder if this is what love feels like.

But still, there are no words.

Kiss the Wind

The leaves
fall off the trees
into the river
rolling at my feet
holding the hand
that's holding on to me
letting the river roll
right by my feet.

My breath is
hanging in the air.
I watch the frozen water
fall everywhere
and hit the ground
with the sweetest of care
no one else to see
those snowflakes fall
but me.

Raindrops
melt off the trees,
telling stories of the
birds and the bees,
passing notes
for only our eyes to read,
thinking our future
is all that we can see.

We're throwing stones
at the pond in the street,
long summer days
swimming at our feet.
Through the rain,
you stay standing next to me.
Though times will change
this is how we will always be,
you right here
with me.

Seasons come
time will go on
and I,
I will smile.
I will
hold on tight
to the hand in mine
Until I
fall back down
Until I
hit this ground
of life
But we'll keep flying
Until we
kiss the wind
goodbye.

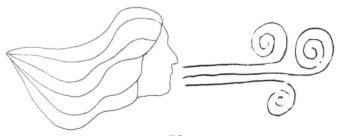

Wallflower

Don't waste your days
Chasing the sunset
Fall into place
With the dawn of the night
Let your words go
Feel through the sorrow
You're too young to know
But we can grow older
tomorrow.

Never & Always

Never underestimate
The impact dreams can have
On your reality.
Let every breath
You take
Fill your heart
With a little more courage
And a little less fear.

Don't be afraid
To open your eyes
To see the beauty
That most see blind
To embrace the new
And keep the old
Close enough forgotten
To make every step
Worth taking twice.
To remember
That no pain is ever gained
From letting love in
Only from shutting
Love out.
Always remember
To let yourself believe
In your day-to-day dreams
And to never underestimate
The power of love
And the impact
Of life.

Keeping Warm

There are no words
Only light from the ground
And a black sky above
The two switched around.
My hands are cold
But the railing is colder
I keep my hands to myself
Feel my heart grow older.
I think of a time
Not long ago
When I'd play outside all day long
And never get cold.
Now I'm always thinking
Of what I can do
To keep myself warm
When left without you.
I try to stand on my own
Without falling down
But I'm already falling
With my feet on the ground.

I'm about to let go
Of something too soon
So I guide my eyes upward
Till I catch the moon.
Without the glow
The snow wouldn't shine
I wouldn't be yours
You wouldn't be mine.
There still are no words
To put into place
All I feel is the cold
All I see is your face.
Then I finally figure out
What I've known in my heart
You're the moon shining
On the white snow
In the dark.

It'll Be Alright

The floor is cold
The window frosty
And old
The story has yet
To be told
It's still being written
Written in gold.

The moon is low
In the sky
The morning
Far from the night
But I know
It'll be alright.

My heart is warm
But my will is
Tired and worn
And my thoughts
Ragged and torn
They're being strengthened
To weather the storm.

The stars above
Align
And for a moment
All is fine
For a moment
No one cries
For a moment
It's alright.

Your hand in mine
Our fingers
Intertwined
And as I look
So deep in your eyes
I see your soul
And know
That you see mine.

Because

I love you because
Our conversations never end
I love you because
You're my very best friend
I love you because
You make the sun brighter
I love you because
You make each night lighter
I love you because
You always keep me safe
I love you because
You're there every day
I love you because
You gave me life
I love you because
You let me be right
I love you because
With you, it's just us.
I guess in the end,
I love you just because.

As Long As I Have You

As long as I have hope
I will always have something to believe in.

As long as I have courage
I will always have something to fight for.

As long as I have friendship
I will always have someone to talk to.

And as long as I have you
I will never be alone.

Inspire You

Let me be your window,
Let me be your light.
Let me be your inspiration,
Let me guide you through the night.
Let me walk beside you,
Let me open up your heart
But never let me live your dreams,
Only you can do that part.

All Sweet Things

Rewrite the moments
That fill your mind
Plan out your days
Spell out your lines
There is only pain
When you have to hide
The feelings you feel
From the one by your side.

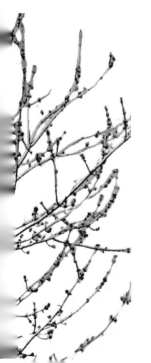

You want to say no
Where he wants to hear yes
You want guarantees
He wants what works best
You can't keep living
By his own broken rules
Running and chasing
Till you fall like a fool
There's somebody better
Waiting for you out there
Who will know how to treat you
With kindness and care.
Sweet bird, sweet child
Know you're never alone
However far gone you are
You can always come home.

Back With Me

I don't know why I do this.
Why I thumb through photographs
trying to see where I belonged
in someone else's past.
I listen to the radio
changing stations till I find
the songs I used to listen to
with someone else in mind.
I wallow in these words
letting nostalgia take me back
letting heartache carry me
to a love I used to have.
As much as I will tend
to let the pain sink in
I will be strong, I will move on
till I'm back with me again.

Together.

Secrets of My Heart

When left alone
With my mind and heart
Alone with all in my head
I picture the end
Forget the start
Drowning in fear, mistrust and dread.
Yet I know a flame
Of passion alone
Left hung out to dry
Is more solemn
Than the darkest night's moon,
The passion, the flame, and I.

There are more words
Than I can use
More thoughts than I can say
Desires hidden
And never proved
Afternoons, evenings, and days.
But there are seven words
I will never forget
Made of letters that won't fall apart
When placed together
They say what's unsaid;
I love you with all of my heart.

This Heart of Mine

These memories we've built
These pieces we've combined
My mind grows fonder
My love grows stronger
In this heart of mine.

Your sun-struck golden hair
Your deep-end blue eyes
Are just a touch of
All I'm sure of
In this heart of mine.

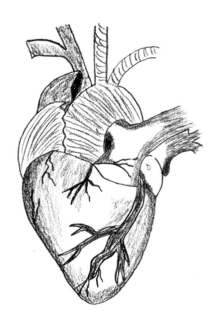

And when it snows in April
Don't let me go
And when the rain falls through the city
Take shelter in my soul
I'll be your hero
Your damsel lost in time
I'll give you everything you need
With this heart of mine.

Untwined

Happiness cannot be found
in the bottom of the glass.
One burned heart alone will heal
but two will turn to ash.
Love should not be taken
with but a grain of sand,
and fingers never twined together
are always waiting for a hand.

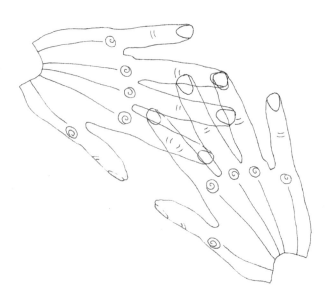

We're taught so many rules
to help guide us through our youth,
but never given the advice
that we will ever use.
Your love has taught me more
than any class that I could take.
If only I had known
that lessons always break.
I know one day I'll see you
as my eyes were meant to see,
I'll look back at all those longings
when the world was you and me.
And my only hope is when I dream
I will not search that glass to find
that long-lost picture of you with me
holding alone my fingers untwined.

Rose Petals

Dried rose petals
from a broken past
Lay fading in this cracked glass jar
Why we give what we know
will never last,
Has an answer less near than far.
Still we follow on this yellowing paper
The map we feel will save
love's lost,
Seeing blindly through
thick fog and vapor
To find the love
we think we want.

We linger on,
our fists clenched tight,
Clinging desperately
to our other half's sleeve,
Only to spend
our darkest of nights
Coveting these mismatched guarantees.
Through all these trials,
time lost and filled,
Through all these maps we travel by,
We search, and search,
and search further still
To find the rose that never dies.

Pressed

Rose petals crisp,
Frail to the touch,
Lost between pages
Of sonnets and rhymes.
My fingers laced
With calluses,
Built on years
Of solitude,
Take hold of
the memories
I thought
you'd gathered
When you smiled
your last
Goodbye.

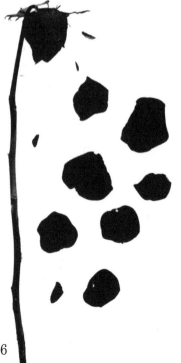

The beating
Of the clock
Hits the back
Of my heart
Like words
Bouncing off the pages.
And love
Burns at my throat
When I realize
All the words I feel inside
You will never see,
That for as many years
As time allows me,
I will clutch,
So gently,
To that rose
in my hand
And think,
Only,
Of you.

The Music of Us

Even in our earliest moments,
Those first glimpses in our eyes,
Every song, every melody
Wrote this story of our lives.

We hold these treasured sounds,
In dances neath the stars,
The lyrics, strung together,
Rhythm, beating in our hearts.

And for as long as the record turns
As long as our ears can see
I'll always listen, and always hear
The music of you and me.

Rhythm of Love

There's no stronger sound
Than a heart beating through
And knowing it's beating
Only for you.
There's no better sight
Than all the memories past
Except seeing to the future
And seeing it will last.
There's no sweeter touch
Than the touch of a hand
That pulls you to your feet
And helps you to stand.

There are no kinder words
Than the ones that you hear
From the one that you love
When they pull you near.
Because there's no greater gift
That could fall from above
Than the language of music
And the rhythm of love.

Something in You

Beauty I once thought I knew
Has fallen deep into the cracks,
Now something in the very thought of you
Shows beauty I thought this world never had.
Something deep inside of you burns,
Pulls me in like rushing water,
And though to pull away is pain endured,
The absence makes my heart grow fonder.
Something in the song that hums
As you sway me, hold me close,
Tells me two hearts can beat as one,
That we can fall back in time as the music slows.
Something about you leaves me breathless,
Runs away with my imagination.
You haunt my dreams, make me restless
Get me lost in all your temptations.

Something in your gentle touch
Weakens my body, strengthens my soul
Never giving me enough,
Never letting my heart grow old.
There are so many beautiful things deep within you,
Some things deeper than my naked eye can see,
You are my hopes.
My dreams.
My inspiration.
And you are all the somethings in the world to me.

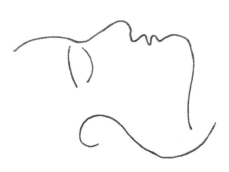

Always & Forever

My darling,
My love,
My most cherished friend.
From the moment that I wake,
Your heart and soul consume me.
With every passing moment,
I find myself lost
In the beauty of you.
Tangled in the passion
Of the love we share,
Of the love I can never lose.
You are my beating heart,
The pulse through my veins,
The light in my darkness.
You are all that I need,
All I cherish and desire.
For darling,
You are my everything,
Always and Forever.

Seasons

Even when crisp leaves fade to dust

Pale snow begins to melt

Flowers grow from ashes

And sunshine falls on green,

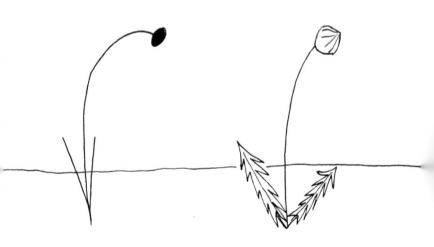

I will be there always,

Somewhere by your side,

Gently tugging on your sleeve

I will always be the wind.

Only You

My love, my darling, my everything,
You mean more to me than any words can say.

You are like air, always around me
Filling my lungs and choking my words
When I breathe you in, I am at peace
As I am yours
And you are my world.

You are like the sun, soothing my soul
The beauty of you, and everything you are,
Kind, generous, and warm
The very best of me,
You are my light
And all my eyes can see.

You are like the stars, filling my eyes
The shimmers of light in the hot, summer sky
And in your eyes, blue as the sea
I see everything I will ever need;
Your heart,
Your hand in mine.

And as long as my two feet stand on this earth
I need not ask the heavens why or how
For I want to be loved by you
And only by you
For longer than time will allow.

Acknowledgements

This book would not be possible without the love and support of so many people.

Thank you to my dear friends, for making me laugh, sharing their stories and couches with me, and always supporting me in whatever I do.

Thank you to my wonderful family. From my grandparents and my aunts and uncles, to my cousins, I'm very fortunate to have had so much support, love, and generosity from them throughout my whole life.

At the heart of my support system are my amazing parents, who love and support me every single day in so many ways. I'm so lucky to have them in my life, and so proud to be their daughter. I love them for many reasons, but most of all I love them just because.

Last but never least, I would like to thank my wonderful husband Danny for loving me, supporting me, and making me feel like I can do anything I set my mind to. Thank you for inspiring so many of the words on these pages. You are my everything, always and forever.

About the Author

Audrey Wilson is the award-winning author of *Wrong Girl Gone* and *Only Human*. She has a BA from Columbia College Chicago, and in addition to winning awards for her poetry and short stories, she has also written over a dozen award-winning short and feature screenplays. Her career in film, radio, and television also earned her a regional Emmy nomination. A Chicago native, Audrey has also spoken professionally at numerous writing events in and around the area. Audrey lives in the Chicago suburbs with her husband, their rescued dog, and cats.

@AudreyWilsonAuthor
www.AudreyWilsonAuthor.com